Tony and Tessa were playing with a cat by
the wall.
Kevin looked at the cat.
'What are you doing with a cat?' asked Kevin.
'When did you get a cat?'

'It is not my cat,' said Tessa.
'It was here when we came to school,'
said Tony.

'Can I play with the cat?' asked Kevin.
'No,' said Tony. 'Look. It is going away now.'

The cat went behind the wall.
But Kevin wanted to play with the cat.
He followed it.
He put the cat in his bag and went into school.

'Look!' said Tessa.
'The cat is inside his bag.'
'You can not play with a cat in school,'
said Tony.
'Give me that cat.'
'No!' said Kevin. 'I am going to keep this cat!'

Kevin took the cat out of his bag.
It jumped out of his hands.
'That will make Mr Belter cross,' said Tony.

6

Mr Belter came in.
The cat was by the window.
'Get that cat out!' he shouted.
'You, boy! Push that window open.'

Tony pushed the window open.
'How about going outside?'
said Tessa to the cat.
The cat looked at Tessa.
It looked at Mr Belter.

The cat did not go outside.
It jumped up on the table.
Mr Belter jumped higher.
He did not like the cat.

9

Tessa grabbed at the cat.
She missed.
It jumped off the table.
Splash! The water went all over Tessa.
It splashed all over the table.
'Kevin Miller. Will you get that cat?' shouted
Mr Belter.

'Do not shout, Mr Belter,'
said the Head Teacher.
'What are you doing? What is all this water?
Are you putting out a fire?'
She looked at Mr Belter.
'Did you do this?' she asked him.

'I did not splash water all over the table,' said Mr Belter.

'It was the cat.'

'Kevin had a cat in his school bag,' said Tony.

'Yes,' said Tessa. 'It was Kevin.'

'What cat?' asked the Head Teacher.
'We do not have a cat. Show me the cat.'
'Look up there,' said Tony.
The Head Teacher looked up.

The cat jumped at the Head Teacher.
She shut her eyes.
She did not like the cat.

14

'Get the police!' shouted the Head Teacher.
She ran out of the room.
Mr Belter followed her.
The cat followed Mr Belter.

Kevin grabbed at the cat.
'Let it go,' said Tony.
'Yes, let it go,' said Tessa.
'The Head Teacher and Mr Belter will look after it.'
Kevin looked at Tony.
Tony looked at Tessa.
They smiled!